Clarinet
Grade 2

Pieces
for Trinity College London exams

2017-2020

Published by
Trinity College London Press
trinitycollege.com

Registered in England
Company no. 09726123

Printed in England by Caligraving Ltd.

7·50

The Zoo-keeper

Duncan Lamont
(born 1931)

Giocoso ♩ = 96

Pleasantry II

from *For Children*

arr. Howard Harrison

Béla Bartók
(1881–1945)

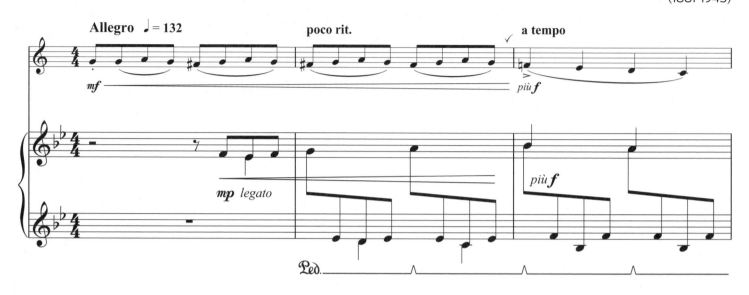

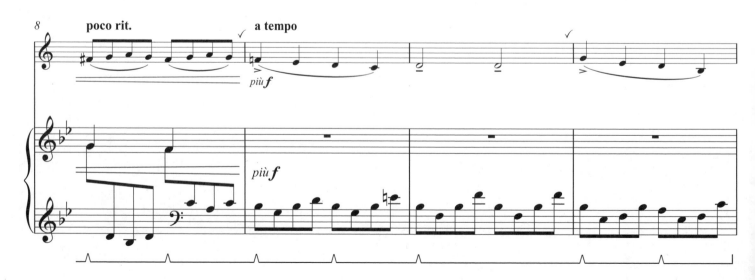

from *Amazing Solos for Clarinet* (ISMN 979-0-060-08469-0)

Clarinet
Grade 2

Pieces

for Trinity College London exams

2017-2020

Published by
Trinity College London Press
trinitycollege.com

Registered in England
Company no. 09726123

Copyright © 2016 Trinity College London Press
First impression, September 2016

Printed in England by Caligraving Ltd.

TCL 016003
ISBN 978-0-85736-553-8

The Zoo-keeper

Duncan Lamont
(born 1931)

Pleasantry II
from *For Children*

arr. Howard Harrison

Béla Bartók
(1881-1945)

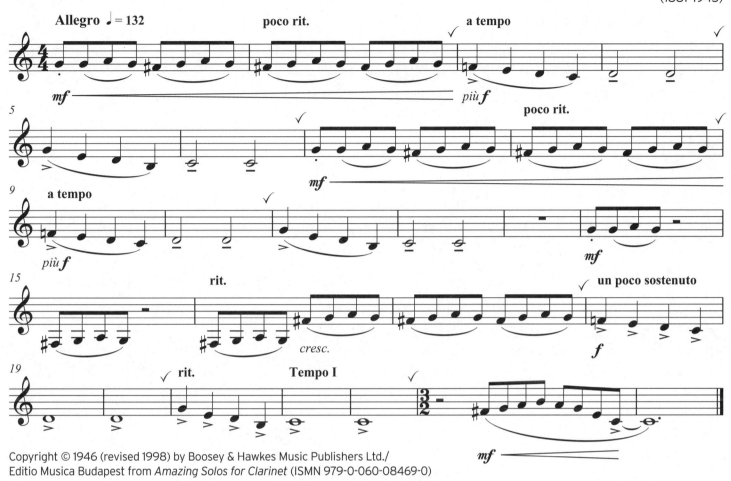

After Hours

Graham Lyons
(born 1936)

Play if enough breath*

* for exam purposes, candidates should play this note for the minimum duration of two bars.

Lilliburlero

arr. Paul Harris

Henry Purcell
(1659-1695)

Moderato [♩ = 144–152]

Shaker Melody

ed. Janet Way

Traditional American

Quietly flowing [♩ = 104–112]

The Skaters' Waltz

arr. Mark Mumford

Emil Waldteufel
(1837–1915)

Study

Friedrich Demnitz
(1845–1890)

Study

Henry Lazarus
(1815-1895)

Tom's Tune

Philip Sparke
(born 1951)

After Hours

Graham Lyons
(born 1936)

Andante tranquillo ♩ = 88

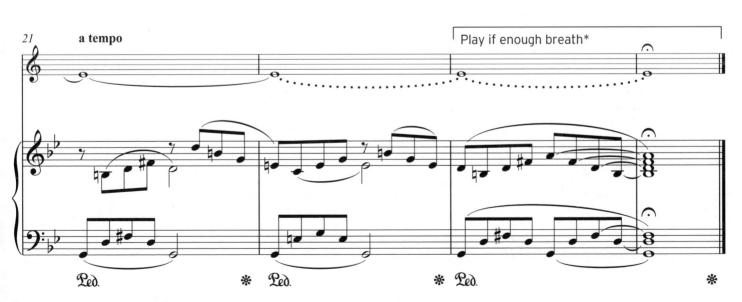

* for exam purposes, candidates should play this note for the minimum duration of two bars.

Lilliburlero

arr. Paul Harris

Henry Purcell
(1659-1695)

Shaker Melody

ed. Janet Way

Traditional American

The Skaters' Waltz

arr. Mark Mumford

Emil Waldteufel
(1837-1915)